SRA OPEN COURT READING

Comprehension and Language Arts Skills

Level 1

Annotated Teacher's Edition

A Division of The McGraw-Hill Companies

Columbus, Ohio

www.sra4kids.com

SRA/McGraw-Hill

A Division of The McGraw·Hill Companies

Send all inquiries to:
SRA/McGraw-Hill
8787 Orion Place
Columbus, OH 43240-4027

Printed in the United States of America.

ISBN 0-07-569523-5

3 4 5 6 7 8 9 POH 06 05 04 03

Table of Contents

Capital Letters

Rule	**Example**
▶ People's names start with capital letters. The word *I* is always written with a capital letter.	▶ Tim Sandy Miller I

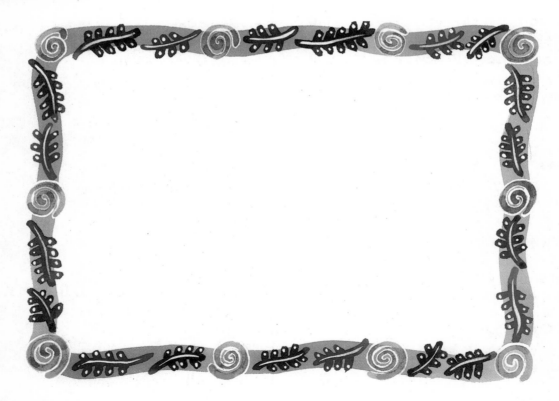

Students should write their first names beginning with capital letters.

Directions: Draw a picture of yourself. Write your name under the picture. Start it with a capital letter.

Practice

▶ **Capital Letters**

Directions: Draw a picture of two people in your family. Write their names under their pictures. Start each name with a capital letter.

Students should write the names of two family members, beginning each with a capital letter.

MECHANICS

UNIT 1 Let's Read! • **Lesson 2** *The Purple Cow*

Writing Words

Rule	**Example**
▶ Letters make words.	▶ cat
	dog

Review words to see how many words
students can write.

UNIT 1   Let's Read! • **Lesson 2** *The Purple Cow*

▶**Writing Words**

Practice

Directions: Write as many words as you can that you see in the pictures.

WRITER'S CRAFT

1.

_____
- - - - - - - - - - - - - -
cat
_____

2.

_____
- - - - - - - - - - - - - -
dog
_____

3.

_____
- - - - - - - - - - - - - -
cow
_____

4.

_____
- - - - - - - - - - - - - -
bat
_____

5.

_____
- - - - - - - - - - - - - -
bug
_____

Name _____ Date _____

Capital Letters: Cities and States

Directions: Four states start with capital A. Write the capital letter.

Rule	Example
▶ Names of cities and states start with capital letters.	▶ New York Ohio Akron Florida Texas Tampa

 **Try It!**

1. Arizona

2. Alabama

3. Arkansas

4. Alaska

Comprehension and Language Arts Skills

▶ **Capital Letters**

Practice

Directions: Draw a picture of your city. Write the name of your city. Write the name of your state. Use capital letters.

Review city and state for correct capitalization.

MECHANICS

Order Words

Directions: Put the pictures in time order. Label them first, next, then, and last.

Rule	**Example**
▶ Some words organize writing.	▶ first next then last

 **Try It!**

_____

first

_____

then

_____

next

_____

last

UNIT 1 Let's Read! • **Lesson 8** *Rhyme Stew*

Directions: Put the pictures in time order. Label them first, next, then, and last.

Practice

last

then

next

first

WRITER'S CRAFT

Sentences

Rule	**Example**
▶ Sentences start with capital letters. Many sentences end with periods.	▶ Frogs leap.

Try It!

1. Birds fly.

2. Dogs run.

3. Fish swim.

4. We have fun.

▶ **Sentences**

Practice

Directions: Put a capital letter at the beginning of each sentence. Put a period at the end of each sentence.

5. Turtles crawl.

6. Cats walk.

7. Rabbits hop.

8. We talk.

MECHANICS

Sentences

Rule	**Example**
▶ Sentences tell a thought.	▶ Mice squeak.

birds   buzz

bees   sing

cows   bark

dogs   moo

1. **Birds sing.**

2. **Bees buzz.**

3. **Cows moo.**

4. **Dogs bark.**

▶ **Sentences**

Practice

Directions: Write sentences using the words in the lists. Put a capital letter at the beginning of each sentence. Put a period at the end of each sentence.

fish   run
mice   swim
deer   fly
birds   jump

_____

5. **Fish swim.** _____

_____

6. **Mice run.** _____

_____

7. **Deer jump.** _____

_____

8. **Birds fly.** _____

UNIT 1 Let's Read! • **Lesson 14** *Mrs. Goose's Baby*

Comparing and Contrasting

Directions: Review "Mrs. Goose's Baby." Discuss each picture and have the children circle A if the picture shows how the goose and chick are alike and D if the picture shows how they are different.

Ⓐ D

A Ⓓ

A Ⓓ

A Ⓓ

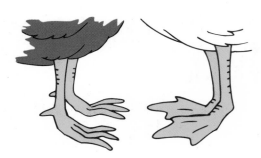

Ⓐ D

A Ⓓ

Comprehension and Language Arts Skills

▶ **Comparing and Contrasting**

Directions: Discuss each picture. Have the students write *A* if the picture shows things that are alike and *D* if it shows things that are different.

COMPREHENSION

Adjectives

Directions: Write the word that describes each picture.

Rule	**Example**
▶ Describing words tell more about something.	▶ A **smart** dog.

sick   big   mad   sad

 big

 sick

 mad

 sad

▶**Adjectives**

Practice

Matt is a sad pup.

Min is sick.

Tom is a big cat.

Mom is not mad.

GRAMMAR AND USAGE

Using Adjectives

Directions: Write an adjective from the box to complete each sentence.

Rule
▶ Adjectives help describe words.

Example
▶ **Cute** raccoon cubs look like their **caring** parents.

 **Try It!**

thick	green	hard	long	weak

1. The turtle has a  **hard** shell.

2. A squirrel has **thick** fur.

3. A frog has **green** skin.

4. A mouse has a **long** tail.

5. Kittens have **weak** legs.

UNIT 2   Animals • **Lesson 2** *Raccoon*

▶**Using Adjectives**

Directions: Draw a picture of yourself. Write words that describe you.

| cute | small | happy | smart |
| careful | friendly | tall | funny |

Answers will vary. Students should draw pictures of themselves and write all words that apply.

WRITER'S CRAFT

Types of Sentences

Rule	**Example**
▸ Some sentences tell.	▸ Deer eat grass.
▸ Some sentences ask.	▸ What do toads eat?
▸ Some sentences show strong feeling.	▸ Let's eat!

Directions: Listen to each sentence. Put a period, question mark, or exclamation point at the end of each sentence.

Try It!

1. I like to eat bananas .

2. Who am I?

3. Eagles catch fish .

4. Watch out!

5. That lion is hungry .

Practice

6. I have a long neck.

7. Who am I?

8. Be careful!

9. Toads eat worms.

10. Yuck!

11. Which animals eat insects?

Directions: Listen to each sentence. Put a period, question mark, or exclamation point at the end of each sentence.

Main Idea and Details

Directions: Circle the picture that does not belong.

Main Idea: Thanksgiving dinner

Details:

▶ **Main Idea and Details**

Directions: Put an X through the picture that does not belong.

Main idea: A baseball game
Details:

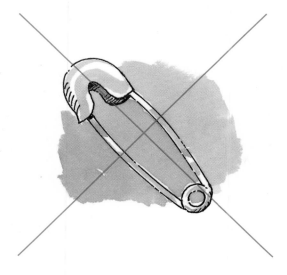

UNIT 2 Animals • **Lesson 8** *Munch Crunch*

Writing Sentences

Rule

► Some sentences tell.
► Some sentences ask.
► Some sentences show strong feeling.

Example

► Deer eat grass.
► What do toads eat?
► Let's eat!

Try It!

1. What do I eat _____ **?** _____

2. I eat _____ **.** _____

3. I love _____ **!** _____

▶ **Writing Sentences**

1. What do snakes eat _____ **?** _____

2. Snakes eat eggs _____ **.** _____

3. They love eggs _____ **!** _____

4. What do eagles eat _____ **?** _____

5. Eagles eat fish _____ **.** _____

6. They love fish _____ **!** _____

WRITER'S CRAFT

Review

▶ **Adjectives**

Directions: Write the word that describes each picture.

tall	small	long	big

1. long

2. small

3. tall

4. big

Comprehension and Language Arts Skills

▶**Review**

▶ Types of Sentences

Directions: Listen to each sentence. Put a period, question mark, or exclamation point at the end of each sentence.

5. I like to buzz.

6. Who am I?

7. I spin a web.

8. Who am I?

9. Watch out!

10. Help, I'm stuck!

11. It's time for lunch.

12. What happened?

GRAMMAR AND USAGE

Writing Descriptions

Directions: Draw a picture of your favorite animal. Write the name of the animal and words to describe it.

> **Rule**
> ▶ Writers describe things.

> **Example**
> ▶ Fish can swim fast. They have tails and fins to help them move.

 **Try It!**

Answers will vary. The description should
match the animal.

UNIT 2 Animals • **Lesson 12** *The Hermit Crab*

► **Writing Descriptions**

Practice

Directions: Draw a picture of yourself. Write your name and words to describe you.

WRITER'S CRAFT

<u>Answers will vary. Students should write</u>
<u>their names and a few words that describe</u>
<u>themselves.</u>

Drawing Conclusions

Directions: Circle the word that fits the picture.

1. Tam and Dan are (not sad, sad).

2. It is (not hot, hot).

3. It is (fun, not fun).

▶ **Drawing Conclusions**

COMPREHENSION

4. The children are at home.   Yes   (No)

5. They are painting.   (Yes)   No

6. They are sad.   Yes   (No)

Possessive Nouns

Directions: Circle the possessive noun that tells who or what has something. Then underline what belongs to the possessive noun.

Rule	**Example**
► Add **'s** to a noun or name to show ownership.	► Jake**'s** hat dog**'s** tail

1. (Pam's) car has a flat tire.

2. We are going to (Grandma's) house.

3. (Danny's) frog won the race.

4. The (bird's) eggs are blue.

▶ **Possessive Nouns**

Directions: Write the words that tell who owns each object. The first one is done for you.

Practice

5. Sue has an apple.

Sue's apple

6. Joe has a truck.

Joe's truck

7. Kate has a ball.

Kate's ball

8. The farmer has a hat.

farmer's hat

9. Dad bakes a pie.

Dad's pie

Staying on Topic

Directions: Read the list. Circle the words that stay on topic. Draw a line through the words that do not belong.

Rule

▶ Writers stay on topic. Writers write lists of words that belong together.

Example

▶ Tools for a Carpenter

hammer

saw

drill

ladder

Try It!

Tools for a Cook

(pan)

(dish)

~~rake~~

(pot)

Students should circle pan, dish, and pot. Students should draw a line through rake.

▶ **Staying on Topic**

Practice

rake	pan	hose	mop	shovel

Tools for a Gardener

1. **rake**

2. **hose**

3. **shovel**

pen	brush	scissors	drill	comb

Tools for a Hairdresser

4. **brush**

5. **comb**

6. **scissors**

WRITER'S CRAFT

Singular and Plural Nouns

Rule	**Example**
▶ Add **s** to a noun to show that there is more than one.	▶ bat bat**s** rug rug**s**

Try It!

1.

2.

3.

4.

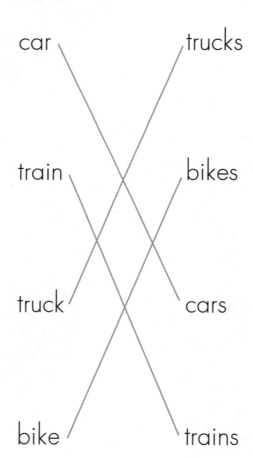

car   trucks

train   bikes

truck   cars

bike   trains

UNIT 3 **Things That Go • Lesson 6** *Song of the Train*

Directions: Look at each picture and read the words. Write a word to make it show more than one.

5. apple

apples

6. dog

dogs

7. carrot

carrots

8. boat

boats

GRAMMAR AND USAGE

Name _____ Date _____

Sensory Details

Directions: Read the sentences. Draw a line under the words that tell how something looks, feels, sounds, smells, and/or tastes.

Rule	**Example**
▶ Writers use words that tell how something looks, feels, sounds, smells, and tastes.	▶ A squirrel has a **long, bushy** tail. **Soft** fur covers its body. Squirrels eat **juicy** berries and **crunchy** nuts. They make **noisy, chirping** sounds.

Try It!

1. A skunk has <u>black</u> fur and a <u>white</u> stripe.

2. Skunks have a <u>stinky</u> spray.

3. Skunks make <u>hissing</u>, <u>growling</u> sounds.

4. They use their <u>strong</u>, <u>sharp</u> claws to dig.

5. Skunks eat <u>soft</u>, <u>chewy</u> worms.

UNIT 3 **Things That Go • Lesson 8** *On the Go*

▶ **Sensory Details**

Practice

Directions: Finish each sentence. Write a word that tells how something looks, sounds, feels, tastes, or smells.

sharp	long	skinny	squeaky	crunchy

_____ _____

6. A mouse has a _____**long**_____, _____**skinny**_____ tail.
_____

7. They eat _____**crunchy**_____ seeds.
_____

8. Mice have _____**sharp**_____ teeth.
_____

9. Mice make _____**squeaky**_____ noises.

WRITER'S CRAFT

Name _____ Date _____

Comparing and Contrasting

Directions: Circle the thing in each row that is different.

1.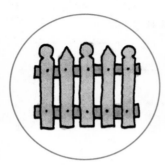

2.

3.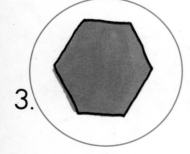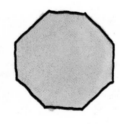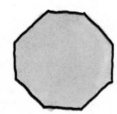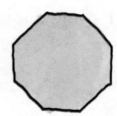

4.   cdgt   cdgt   cgdt   cdgt

Directions: Circle the word or words that tell how the animals are alike.

COMPREHENSION

▶**Comparing and Contrasting**

5. (four legs)   pet

  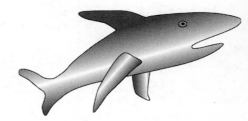

6.   legs   (no legs)

7. (live in nest)   have fur

UNIT 3 **Things That Go • Lesson 11** *On the Go*

Directions: Circle the possessive noun that tells who or what has something. Then write who or what owns something on the line. The first one is done for you.

▶ Review

▶ Possessive Nouns

1. The (train's) whistle is loud.

train

2. (Papa's) car is red.

Papa

3. (Mary's) horse runs fast.

Mary

4. This is (Jason's) wagon.

Jason

5. (Jim's) boat has a white sail.

Jim

Comprehension and Language Arts Skills

UNIT 3 **Things That Go • Lesson II** *On the Go*

Singular and Plural Nouns ▶Review

6. (snake)   snakes

7. pig   (pigs)

8. ant   (ants)

9. frog   (frogs)

10. duck   (ducks)

11. (cow)   cows

GRAMMAR AND USAGE

Order Words

Directions: Look at the pictures. Draw a line from the picture to the correct word.

Rule	**Example**
▶ Order words tell the order things happen.	▶ **First** you dig a hole.
	Next you put in a seed.
	Then you cover the seed with dirt.
	Last you water the seed.

Try It!

1.

first

2.

next

3.

last

► **Order Words**

WRITER'S CRAFT

Practice

Directions: Look at each picture. Write the correct word on the line.

| Then | Last | First |

4. **_First_** we think of an idea.

5. **_Then_** we write.

6. **_Last_** we share our writing.

Capitalization

Rule	Example
▶ Days and months begin with capital letters.	▶ **S**unday June

1. Sam and Liz rode bikes on (saturday).

2. They went to the park on (sunday).

3. School starts on (monday), (august) 29.

4. Sam's birthday is in (october).

MECHANICS

▶**Capitalization**

Practice

Directions: Circle the letter that needs to be a capital. Write the word using a capital letter.

5. ⓜonday   Monday

6. ⓙuly   July

7. ⓜarch   March

8. ⓦednesday   Wednesday

9. ⓝovember   November

10. ⓐugust   August

Classifying

Directions: Draw lines connecting the pairs of objects that belong together.

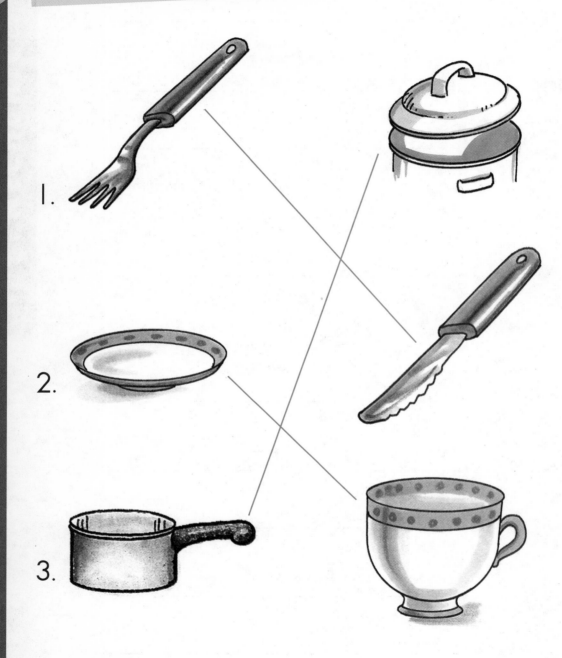

1.

2.

3.

Comprehension and Language Arts Skills

▶ **Classifying**

Directions: Draw a line from each animal on the left to the one that is most similar on the right.

4.

5.

6.

7.

Who, What, Where, and When

Rule	**Example**
▶Writers answer the questions who, what, where, and when to be sure they tell about everything.	Who: **Teachers** are workers. What: They **teach children how to read.** Where: They work **in schools.** When: They work **all day long.**

Try It!

1. The man    when

2. mops the floor   where

3. every night   who

4. at the shop.   what

▶ **Who, What, Where, and When**

WRITER'S CRAFT

Directions: Read each sentence. Look at the underlined words. Write the question word that it answers.

Practice

who	what	where	when

5. We mail letters at a <u>post office</u>.

where

6. The post office opens <u>in the morning</u>.

when

7. Workers <u>sort the letters</u>.

what

8. A <u>letter carrier</u> brings mail to your house.

who

End Punctuation

Directions: Read each sentence. Draw a line to the correct end mark.

Rule
▶ Sentences end with . or ? or !

Example
▶ Where is the moon?
It is in the sky.
See how big it looks!

Try It!

1. Who has a dog   !

2. Tomás has a dog   ?

3. The dog is bigger than Tomás   .

4. Where is the frog   .

5. The frog is on the log   ?

6. Hop away frog   !

UNIT 4 Our Neighborhood at Work • **Lesson 6** *Firefighters*

▶ **End Punctuation**

Practice

7. Today I will ride a bus ___.___

8. Where will the bus go ___?___

9. It is the first day of school ___.___

10. I am excited ___!___

11. I like school ___.___

12. How do you get to school ___?___

MECHANICS

A Friendly Letter

Directions: Circle the date with a blue crayon. Circle the greeting in red. Circle the message in green. Circle the closing in black. Circle the writer's name in brown.

▶Friendly letters have five parts.

Date	June 19, 2001
Greeting	Dear Amy,
Message	We saw the Liberty Bell. It weighs more than a ton! It has a crack. They don't ring it anymore.
Closing	Your friend,
Your Name	Jennifer

Try It!

March 2, 2004

Dear Joe,

My school had a book sale. I got three new books. Would you like to read my books?

Your friend,
Ellie

► **A Friendly Letter**

WRITER'S CRAFT

Practice

We went to Fort Clatsop.   May 12, 2002
The rangers showed us how candles and
shoes were made.
We watched them build a boat!
Your friend,   Drew   Dear Pat,

_____

May 12, 2002

Dear Pat,

  **We went to Fort Clatsop. The rangers
showed us how candles and shoes were
made. We watched them build a boat!**

Your friend,
Drew

_____

_____

▶ Review

▶ Capitalization

Directions: Read each sentence. Write the word that should be capitalized on the line.

1. Rose has a birthday in may.

May

2. Her party is friday.

Friday

3. january is the coldest month.

January

4. It rains a lot in april.

April

5. We have music class on tuesday.

Tuesday

6. On thursday we go to art class.

Thursday

Comprehension and Language Arts Skills

UNIT 4 **Our Neighborhood at Work • Lesson II** *Worksong*

▶ **End Punctuation**   ▶ **Review**

Directions: Read the story. Write the correct end marks.

I like to walk down my street __.__ Would

you like to walk with me __?__ I can see flowers

and trees __.__ Who moved into the red house __?__

Maybe a new friend lives there __! or .__ Friends are

nice __.__ That was a long walk __! or .__ Thank you

for walking with me __.__ I am tired __! or .__

Comprehension and Language Arts Skills   **UNIT 4 • Lesson II** **57**

MECHANICS

Audience and Purpose

Rule	**Example**
▶Writers think about who is going to read their writing. They think about what they want to tell.	▶A coach writes game rules for the players. ▶A teacher writes a note to a parent. ▶A boy writes an invitation to invite friends to a party.

Try It!

1. someone who gave a gift   tell them about your report

2. your class   write about your feelings

3. your parent ——————— write a story about your family

4. yourself   thank them for a gift

► **Audience and Purpose**

 **Practice**

teacher   friend   librarian   yourself   pet store owner

5. journal page   **yourself**

6. invitation to a party   **friend**

7. report about plants   **teacher**

8. questions about dogs   **pet store owner**

9. list of books   **librarian**

WRITER'S CRAFT

Longer Sentences

Rule

▶Writers write longer sentences to tell more. They write words that tell how, when, and where.

Example

▶Eagles eat fish.

How: Eagles eat fish **quickly.**

When: Eagles eat fish **often.**

Where: Eagles eat fish **out of** the water.

Try It!

1. Otters swim <u>fast.</u>

2. Otters slide <u>down muddy hills.</u>

3. Otters play <u>every day.</u>

► **Longer Sentences**

Directions: Read the first sentence. Use the words in the box to make each sentence longer. Add words that tell how, when, or where.

Practice

| on my lap | softly | sometimes |

My cat purrs. _____

How: 4. My cat purrs **softly** _____.

When: 5. My cat purrs **sometimes** _____.

Where: 6. My cat purrs **on my lap** _____.

| in the sky | every day | quickly |

Birds fly. _____

How: 7. Birds fly **quickly** _____.

When: 8. Birds fly **every day** _____.

Where: 9. Birds fly **in the sky** _____.

WRITER'S CRAFT

Adjectives

Directions: Read each sentence. Draw a line to the picture that it describes.

Rule	**Example**
▶ Adjectives are words used to describe nouns.	▶ The dog is *big.* That is a *big* dog.

Try It!

1. The pan is hot.

2. The gray whales swim.

3. Sam has a yellow ball.

4. We filled the big pot.

▶**Adjectives**

Practice

new	tall	three	gold	wet

_____

5. The ____three____ mice run away.

_____

6. Becky's coat has ____gold____ buttons.

_____

7. There are ____tall____ buildings in the city.

_____

8. Dan took off his ____wet____ shoes.

_____

9. I rode my ____new____ bike in the park.

GRAMMAR AND USAGE

Main Idea and Details

Main Idea: Day at the Beach

Details:

▶ **Main Idea and Details**

Directions: Put an X through the picture that does not belong.

Main Idea: Nighttime
Details:

Order Words

Directions: Read the sentences. Draw a line under the order words.

Rule

▶ Order words tell the order things happen.

Example

▶ **First,** the batter holds the bat.
Next, the pitcher throws the ball.
Then, the batter swings the bat.
Last, the batter hits the ball and runs to first base.

 **Try It!**

1. <u>First</u>, the runner stretches.

2. <u>Then</u>, she goes to the starting line.

3. <u>Next</u>, she waits to hear the starting bell.

4. <u>Last</u>, she starts running.

UNIT 5 Weather • **Lesson 3** *When a Storm Comes Up*

▶ **Order Words**

Practice

Next	First	Last	Then

5. ____**First**____, Matt makes a sandwich.

6. **Next (or Then)**, he wraps it in plastic.

7. **Then (or Next)**, he gets an apple and raisins.

8. ____**Last**____, he puts everything in a bag.

WRITER'S CRAFT

UNIT 5 Weather • **Lesson 6** *Listen to the Rain*

▶ Verbs

Rule	**Example**
▶ Verbs show action.	▶ We **walk** to school.
	She **rides** the bus.

Try It!

spins	run	smiles	talk

1. _____ **smiles**

_____

2. _____ **run**

3. _____ **spins**

4. _____ **talk**

UNIT 5 Weather • **Lesson 6** *Listen to the Rain*

▶**Verbs**

Practice

Directions: Read the sentences. Circle the word that shows action in each sentence.

5. A tree (grows) in the yard.

6. The wind (blows) the branches.

7. Leaves (fall) from the tree.

8. Dad (rakes) the leaves.

9. Jake (helps) Kayla.

10. The children (put) the leaves in the bag.

Review

Adjectives

Directions: Read each sentence. Draw a line under the words that describe a noun. Circle the noun that they describe.

1. My family takes fun (trips).

2. I put on my new (boots).

3. We climbed a steep (hill).

4. Dad made a tasty (lunch).

5. We sat by a big old (tree).

▶ **Verbs**   ▶ **Review**

Directions: Read the words in the box. Choose the verb that fits each sentence. Write the verb on the line.

wins	kicks	runs	cheers	ties

6. Joshua _____ **ties** _____ his shoe.

7. Ashley _____ **kicks** _____ the ball.

8. She _____ **runs** _____ down the field.

9. The crowd _____ **cheers** _____ .

10. Our team _____ **wins** _____ the game!

GRAMMAR AND USAGE

Commas in a Series

Directions: Read each sentence. Write the commas where they belong.

Rule	Example
▶ Commas are used in lists of three or more.	▶ Lauren, Nathan, and Trevor are in my class.

Try It!

1. Mom, Dad, and I went to the store.

2. We bought milk, eggs, butter, and flour.

3. I helped Mom measure, pour, and mix the batter.

4. Dad and I rinsed, washed, and dried the dishes.

5. We ate pancakes with fruit, milk, and juice.

▶ **Commas in a Series**

Practice

Directions: Read the story. Write commas where they belong so that the story is easier to read and understand.

MECHANICS

Shane, Ryan, and Amber went to camp. The camp had a lake, trees, and hills. The children played soccer, baseball, and basketball. They also liked to hike, swim, and sing songs. It was a fun, happy, and busy week.

▶ Classifying

Directions: Write the word that goes with each object.

truck	bird	bee
jet	car	bike

wheels   wings

1. **car** _____   4. **bird** _____

2. **bike** _____   5. **jet** _____

3. **truck** _____   6. **bee** _____

▶ **Classifying**

Directions: Choose two words that belong together and write them on the lines.

sock	brush	cookies	foot
milk	bat	comb	ball

_____   _____

7. _____ **comb** _____ and _____ **brush** _____

_____   _____

8. _____ **milk** _____ and _____ **cookies** _____

_____   _____

9. _____ **foot** _____ and _____ **sock** _____

_____   _____

10. _____ **bat** _____ and _____ **ball** _____

COMPREHENSION

A Paragraph That Explains

Directions: Read the sentences. Write the numbers 1, 2, 3, 4, and 5 to tell the order the sentences should be written in a paragraph.

Rule

▶ Writers use paragraphs to explain. The first sentence tells what the writer will explain. The other sentences tell what happens in the correct order.

Teacher: Read the following paragraph to students as an example. *A crow eats seeds. First it finds a nut. Next it flies to the top of a pole. Then it drops the nut to break it. Last it flies down to get the seed out of the broken nutshell.*

1. __5__ Last the robin pulls the worm out of the ground.

2. __1__ A robin eats worms.

3. __2__ First the robin walks on the grass.

4. __3__ Next the robin stops walking.

5. __4__ Then the robin hears a worm.

▶**A Paragraph That Explains**

WRITER'S CRAFT

Directions: Read the sentences. Write a sentence that tells what they explain. Then write all of the sentences in the form of a paragraph.

Practice

First I get a can of dog food.
Then I open the can.
Next I pour the food in the dish.
Last my dog eats.

Students should write a topic sentence that tells what the above sentences explain. Answers may include: I feed my dog every day. I give my dog dog food. Students should write the sentences in paragraph form, in the order they appear.

Capitalization: Cities and States

Rule	**Example**
▶ The names of cities and states always begin with a capital letter.	▶ Madison, Wisconsin

Try It!

1. (Columbus, Ohio)
   columbus, ohio

2. (Reno, Nevada)
   reno, nevada

3. austin, texas
   (Austin, Texas)

4. (Springfield, Illinois)
   springfield, Illinois

Capitalization: Cities and States

MECHANICS

Practice

Directions: Read each sentence. Underline the word or words that should begin with a capital letter. Write the capital letters above the words.

5. The Statue of Liberty is in <u>N</u> <u>Y</u>ew york.

6. Yellowstone National Park is in <u>W</u>yoming.

7. The Sears Tower in <u>C</u>hicago is the tallest building in the world.

8. The Space Needle in <u>S</u>eattle was left after a world's fair.

9. Our national anthem was written in <u>B</u>altimore, Maryland.

10. In <u>A</u>rizona you can visit the Grand Canyon.

Place and Location Words

Directions: Look at each picture. Draw a line to the words that tell where.

Rule	**Example**
▶ Writers use words that tell exactly where people, places, and things are.	▶ The duck is **in** the water. This bridge is **over** the water. The table is **behind** the cat.

Try It!

1.    on the log

2.   in the nest

3.   beside the fishbowl

UNIT 6 Journeys • **Lesson 8** *Me On the Map*

▶ **Place and Location Words**

Practice

| over | on | between | under | in | behind |

4. The squirrel sits ___**on**___ the log.

5. A cat walks ___**between**___ the dishes.

6. The dog stands ___**behind**___ the fence.

7. The gerbil hides ___**in**___ the paper.

8. The jellyfish swims ___**over**___ the shell.

9. A bird finds a worm ___**under**___ a tree.

Comprehension and Language Arts Skills

WRITER'S CRAFT

Making Inferences

Directions: Look at the picture. Based on the clues in the picture, describe what's happening. Write three sentences. Answers will vary.

_____

It is fall.
_____

_____

The girl and boy are raking the leaves.
_____

_____

The leaves fell off the trees.
_____

_____

_____

Name _____ Date _____

Name _____ Date _____

UNIT 6 **Journeys • Lesson II** *The Special Day*

▶ Making Inferences

It is warm outside.

The boys and girls are playing.

The boys and girls are happy.

COMPREHENSION

Review

Commas in a Series

1. I went to the beach with Uncle Tim, Aunt Ann, and my cousin Scott.

2. I brought my shovel, pail, and sand toys.

3. Scott and I played in the soft, clean, white sand.

4. Aunt Ann brought grapes, cherries, and plums for snacks.

5. We swam, played, and listened to the waves all day long.

6. Everyone was hot, tired, and happy.

▶ Capitalization: Cities and States   ▶ Review

Directions: Read each sentence. Draw a line under the 10 words that name cities and states that should begin with a capital letter. Write the correct capital letter above the word.

MECHANICS

          G   C
1. Pete lives in <u>grove</u> <u>city</u>, Ohio.

                  C   M
2. His grandma lives in <u>columbia</u>, <u>maryland</u>.

                                  P
3. Pete's family drives through <u>pennsylvania</u> to
   get to Grandma's house.

                      O   P
4. Pete's cousin lives in <u>oak</u> <u>park</u>, Illinois.

                             I
5. Pete's family drives through <u>indiana</u> to get to
   his cousin's house.

                                       V
6. Next winter everyone will go skiing in <u>vail</u>,
   C
   <u>colorado</u>.

Form of a Paragraph

Rule	**Example**
▶ Writers use sentences that go together to write a paragraph. 	▶ Helicopters are used to help people. They carry hurt people to hospitals. They take food to places people can't go. They can take heavy equipment to a rooftop. Helicopters are very useful.

 **Try It!**

Trains have many cars. Sleeper cars have beds where people can sleep. Dining cars are where people can eat. ~~We ate carrots for dinner.~~ Coaches are cars where people can sit and look out the windows. A train has cars for all the passengers.

▶ **Form of a Paragraph**

WRITER'S CRAFT

Directions: Read the sentences. Finish the paragraph by writing the sentences that go together.

Practice

A bike has many parts.
A bike has a seat.
It has two wheels.
It has handlebars.
I ride the bus to school.
All parts of a bike work together.
A car has four wheels.

A bike has many

parts. A bike has a seat. It has two wheels. It has handlebars. All parts of a bike work together.

_____

_____

_____

_____

Past Tense Verbs

Rule

▶ Add *-ed* to a verb to show that something already happened.

▶ Some verbs change to show that something already happened. They don't use *-ed*.

Example

▶ Yesterday I **walked** with Lisa.

▶ Cara sings a song. Yesterday she **sang** a song.

Look at each picture. Circle the verb that tells that it already happened.

1. jump (jumped)

2. clap (clapped)

3. see (saw)

4. eat (ate)

UNIT 7 Keep Trying • **Lesson I** *Unit Introduction*

▶**Past Tense Verbs**

Practice

Read the sentence. Write the verb that tells that something already happened.

5. Billy and I ___**went**___ to the fair.

   go   went

6. Billy ___**played**___ games.

   played   plays

7. He ___**pinned**___ the tail on the donkey.

   pin   pinned

8. We ___**saw**___ a clown.

   saw   see

GRAMMAR AND USAGE

Exact Words

Rule	**Example**
▶Writers write exact words to help readers understand. 	▶A **honeybee hovers** over the **bright yellow** flower. Its **long, skinny** tongue **sucks** up **sweet** nectar.

Try It!

Read the sentence. Draw a line under the exact words.

1. The dragonfly's shiny, blue body sparkles in the bright sunlight.

2. Its four, long wings flutter rapidly.

3. It skims across the quiet pond.

4. You hear a soft rattle as the beautiful dragonfly darts here and there.

UNIT 7 Keep Trying • **Lesson 2** *The Itsy Bitsy Spider*

▶ **Exact Words**

Practice

Look at the picture. Write exact words
that tell about it.

_____

The students should write exact words which

include nouns, adjectives, adverbs, or vivid

verbs. Answers may include soft fuzzy fur;

fluffy orange fur; bushy tail; playful; tangled in

yarn; pounces on yarn; long black stripes, tiny

white feet, and so on.

_____

_____

_____

_____

WRITER'S CRAFT

Cause and Effect

Read each sentence. Circle the best cause, **a** or **b**.

1. Jenny ran and grabbed a paper towel.
   - **a.** She had spilled some juice.
   - **b.** She needed to write a note.

2. Tom blew out all six candles on the cake.
   - **a.** He was afraid of fire.
   - **b.** It was his birthday.

3. Dad bought a new rake.
   - **a.** The old rake was broken.
   - **b.** He liked its blue color.

4. Mom took Shane to the dentist.
   - **a.** He had a chipped tooth.
   - **b.** It was on the way to the store.

Comprehension and Language Arts Skills

UNIT 7 Keep Trying • **Lesson 3** *The Kite*

▶ **Cause and Effect**

COMPREHENSION

Match the effects and causes.

Effects	**Causes**

5. Everyone cheered.

6. There was a thunderstorm.

7. Mom gave Amy some juice.

8. Our car suddenly stopped.

9. Barbara carried the box for Meg.

10. We warmed our hands by the campfire.

11. Mom handed Georgia some tape.

She was thirsty.

We had run out of gas.

Andy won the race.

It was too heavy for her.

The sky became very dark.

She needed to wrap a package.

It was so cold.

Pronouns

Rule	Example
▶ A pronoun takes the place of a noun.	▶ Sam poured the juice. **He** poured **it**.

Try It!

Look at the picture. Read the sentence.
Write the correct pronoun on the line.

it	they	we	he	him	she	I

1. I can kick ____**it**____ very far.

2. ____**She**____ is on my team.

3. ____**He**____ is my coach.

UNIT 7 Keep Trying • **Lesson 3** *The Kite*

▶ **Pronouns**

GRAMMAR AND USAGE

Practice

Read each pair of sentences. Write the correct pronoun in the blank.

| she | he | her | them | I |

4. My name is Kim.

   I am seven years old.

5. Janet likes to paint.

   She is an artist.

6. Chad lives next door.

   He likes to draw.

7. Janet and Chad are going to an art show.

   I am going with **them** .

Staying on Topic

Rule	**Example**
▶Writers stay on the topic. 	▶ I wanted to learn how to ride a bike. Every time I tried to ride, I fell. I wanted to quit. Then my brother helped me. Now I can ride my bike!

 **Try It!**

Read the paragraph. Draw a line through the sentence that does not belong.

I wrote a story about my friend Jen. I told about the time she helped me paint a picture. ~~She has three cats.~~ I read my story to the class.

UNIT 7 Keep Trying • **Lesson 3** *The Kite*

▶ **Staying on Topic**

Practice

Write a paragraph using the sentences
that stay on topic.

My family visited the Grand Canyon.
We walked on the trails.
I have new shoes.
We rode a raft down the river.
My sister is nine.
We rode horses.
The Grand Canyon is a fun place to go.

_____

**My family visited the Grand Canyon. We
walked on the trails. We rode a raft down the
river. We rode horses. The Grand Canyon is a
fun place to go.**

_____

_____

_____

_____

WRITER'S CRAFT

Drawing Conclusions

Look at the picture. Complete each sentence by circling the best word.

1. The children are (playing, working).

2. It is (winter, summer).

3. The children are having (fun, no fun).

UNIT 7 Keep Trying • **Lesson 4** *The Garden*

▶Drawing Conclusions

COMPREHENSION

Look at the picture. Find the best answer. Circle a, b, or c.

4. Joy is smiling because:

   (a. She has an ice cream cone.)

   b. She just went to the doctor.

   c. She is petting a dog.

5. Min is upset because:

   a. She is going to the park.

   (b. She feels sick.)

   c. She lost her doll.

Possessive Pronouns

Rule	Example
▶ A possessive pronoun takes the place of a possessive noun. It shows ownership.	▶ Ty's shoes are black. **Her** shoes are black.

Read each sentence. Circle the
correct possessive pronoun. Write it on the line.

1. I live in a house on Maple Street.

_____

- - - - - -

_____ house is green.   (My)   Its

2. Grandma is bringing a puppy.

_____

- - - - - -

_____ name is Max.   Her   (Its)

▶Possessive Pronouns

Practice

Look at the picture. Read the sentence.
Write the possessive pronoun and what
is owned.

my	your	her	his	its

3. Maria has a book.   **her book**

4. Kin has a ball.   **his ball**

5. The cat has a tail.   **its tail**

6. I have a balloon.   **my balloon**

7. You have an apple.   **your apple**

GRAMMAR AND USAGE

▶Sentences

Rule	**Example**
▶Writers write complete sentences. A sentence has a naming part and an action part. Every sentence begins with a capital letter and ends with an end mark.	▶Raindrops splash on the ground. A lot of rain makes a mud puddle.

Try It!

Draw a line to match the sentence parts to make a complete sentence.

1. The sun   blow.

2. Snowflakes   rumbles.

3. Strong winds   shines.

4. Thunder   fall.

▶ Sentences

Practice

Look at the picture. Write words that complete each sentence.

5. Sam and Liz _____

Answers will vary. Students should complete the sentences by writing an appropriate subject or predicate. The sentences should begin with a capital letter and end with an end mark.

6. _____ was a sunny day.

_____

7. Sam's bike _____

_____

8. _____ rode to the school.

WRITER'S CRAFT

Main Idea and Details

Read the main idea. Circle the picture
that does not belong.

Main Idea: Nature/Plants
Details:

▶ **Main Idea and Details**

Read the main idea. Put an **X** on the
picture that does not belong.

Main Idea: Insects
Details:

Adjectives That Compare

Rule	**Example**
▶ Add *-er* to a describing word to compare two things. Add *-est* to a describing word to compare more than two things.	▶ I am **older** than my brother. Mom is the **oldest** in our family.

 **Try It!**

Add *-er* and *-est* to make describing words that compare.

1. tall   **taller**   **tallest**

2. short   **shorter**   **shortest**

3. fast   **faster**   **fastest**

4. slow   **slower**   **slowest**

▶ **Adjectives That Compare**

Practice

Read each sentence. Write the correct word on the line.

5. Henry is _____**taller**_____ than Fran.
taller   tallest

6. Fran has the _____**longest**_____ hair of all.
longer   longest

7. I am the _____**tallest**_____ person in my class.
taller   tallest

8. Fran's cat is _____**bigger**_____ than Henry's fish.
big   bigger

9. My dog is the _____**biggest**_____ pet of all.
bigger   biggest

GRAMMAR AND USAGE

Longer Sentences

Rule

▶Writers write longer sentences to tell more. They use words that tell how, where, and when.

Example

▶Stars shine.
How: Stars shine **brightly.**
When: Stars shine at **night.**
Where: Stars shine **everywhere.**

 **Try It!**

Read the sentences. Circle the words that tell how, when, or where.

1. The plane lands (perfectly).

2. The plane lands (at the airport).

3. The plane lands (soon).

▶**Longer Sentences**

Practice

Read the sentence. Use the words in
the box to make the sentence longer.
Truck drivers travel.

| around the country   every week   safely |

4. How: ___ Truck drivers travel safely. ___

_____

_____

5. When: ___ Truck drivers travel every week. ___

_____

_____

6. Where: ___ Truck drivers travel around the country. ___

_____

_____

WRITER'S CRAFT

Sequence

Put the sentences in order. Use 1–4.

_____

__1__ Jan and Pete wake up.

_____

__4__ Then Pete and Jan leave for school.

_____

__3__ Jan puts on her coat.

_____

__2__ Pete brushes his teeth.

UNIT 7 Keep Trying • **Lesson 7** *The Hare and the Tortoise*

▶**Sequence**

COMPREHENSION

Put the sentences in order using 1–6.

_____

__2__ Jill gave the cat some food.

_____

__1__ The cat woke Jill up in the morning.

__5__ Jill went outside to play.

__4__ After breakfast Jill got dressed and put on her shoes.

__3__ After the cat ate some food, it sat on Jill's lap while she ate her cereal.

__6__ Jill's mother asked her to come inside for dinner.

Review

▶ ## Past Tense Verbs

Read each sentence. Circle the word
that tells what happened in the past.

1. My ball (rolled) away.

2. I (looked) for it all day.

3. I (crawled) under the bed.

4. I (climbed) over the chair.

5. I (ran) down the stairs.

6. Then I (opened) the door.

7. I (found) my ball!

UNIT 7 Keep Trying • **Lesson 7** *The Hare and the Tortoise*

▶ **Pronouns, Possessive Pronouns, and Adjectives That Compare**

▶ **Review**

GRAMMAR AND USAGE

Read the paragraph. Draw a box around the possessive pronouns. Circle the other pronouns. Underline the three adjectives that compare.

I you we they us it her my

Grant Park has the <u>tallest</u> trees in town. I went to the park with my friend. Her name is Amy. The park was a mess. We wanted to clean it up. We saw my friends Jake and Luke. They are <u>older</u> than I am. They helped us pick up trash in the park. Now it is the <u>cleanest</u> park in town.

Dialogue

Rule	Example
▶The exact words a character speaks are called dialogue. Write quotation marks at the beginning and end of the exact words someone says.	▶Jake asked, "Who was Johnny Appleseed?" Mr. Foster replied, "He was a pioneer who planted many apple trees."

 **Try It!** Read the sentence. Draw a line under the words that are said. Draw a circle around who is speaking.

1. "I read a book about Benjamin Franklin," said Pat.

2. "He invented a new kind of glasses," said Aaron.

3. "He also invented the heating stove," added Pat.

▶ **Dialogue**

Practice

Write quotation marks at the beginning
and end of the words someone says.

4. "I think I'll write a make-believe story,"
   said Randy.

5. "Are you going to write a scary story?"
   asked Devin.

6. "Why don't you write a story about a
   space ship?" asked Michelle.

7. "No, I think I'll write about an animal
   that can talk," answered Randy.

8. "That's a good idea," said Michelle.

9. "You could write about a talking
   skunk!" exclaimed Devin.

10. "Or you could write about a talking
    lizard!" added Michelle.

WRITER'S CRAFT

Kinds of Sentences

Rule	Example
▶ A sentence that tells something ends with a period.	▶ I hit the ball.
▶ A sentence that asks something ends with a question mark.	▶ How far did it go?
▶ A sentence that shows strong feeling ends with an exclamation point.	▶ I hit a home run!

 **Try It!** Read each sentence. Write the end mark that goes with each kind of sentence.

1. I like to play games ___.___

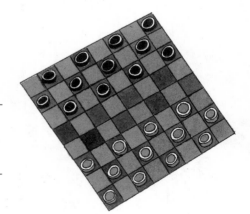

2. What is your favorite game ___?___

3. I love checkers ___!___

▶ **Kinds of Sentences**

GRAMMAR AND USAGE

Practice

4. Circle the telling sentence.

Who ran in the race?

(I ran in the race.)

5. Circle the asking sentence.

Cara plays soccer.

(Did you see her play?)

6. Circle the sentence that shows strong feeling.

My dad is proud of me.

(He gave me a big hug!)

UNIT 8 **Games • Lesson 2** *A Game Called Piggle*

Sequence

Circle the word that tells about time.

1. They must leave for school (now).

2. We can play (after) we do the dishes.

3. Beth sang (as) Chuck played the guitar.

4. The calf stayed in the barn (during) the storm.

5. Kevin fed our cat (while) we went on a trip.

6. Grandpa will arrive very (soon).

7. Sam washed the car (before) he left.

8. Tina has grown an inch (since) June.

▶Sequence

Look at the picture. Put the sentences in order. Use 1–4.

_____ **3** Soon he is at the pond.

_____ **1** The turtle wakes up as the sun rises.

_____ **4** Then he slips into the water.

_____ **2** Slowly he walks along the path until he reaches the pond.

COMPREHENSION

Sensory Details

> **Rule**
>
> ▶ Writers use words that tell how something looks, feels, sounds, smells, and tastes. Writers want readers to have good clear pictures in their minds.
>
> **Example**
>
> ▶ I walked on the **old wooden** bridge.
> ▶ **Cool** water flows in the river.

 **Try It!** Draw a line under the words that tell how something looks, feels, sounds, tastes, or smells.

1. The ring had a <u>beautiful</u>, <u>sparkling</u> stone.

2. Do you hear the horse's <u>clomping</u> hooves?

3. <u>Crisp</u>, <u>warm</u> popcorn makes a good snack.

4. Wear a <u>heavy</u> coat on the <u>cold</u>, <u>damp</u> mornings.

▶ **Sensory Details**

Practice

Write words to finish the sentences.

| sandy   cool   bumpy   fluffy   white   colorful |

_____

5. We walked on the ____**sandy**____ beach.

6. We swam in the ____**cool**____ water.

7. We picked up _____**colorful**_____ ,

____**bumpy**____ shells.

8. We looked up at the ____**fluffy**____ ,

____**white**____ clouds.

WRITER'S CRAFT

Comparing and Contrasting

Look at each picture. Circle the phrase
that tells about the pictures.

1. (things to eat)   fruits and vegetables

2. three pictures of girls   (people drinking from cups)

UNIT 8 Games • **Lesson 3** *Jafta*

► **Comparing and Contrasting**

Look at each picture. Circle the phrase that tells about the pictures.

3. (things that grow)   plants with flowers

4. animals with fur   (animals with teeth)

5. animals that live on farms   (things that people can ride)

COMPREHENSION

Sentence Parts

Rule	Example
▶ Every sentence has two parts. The **naming part** tells who or what. The **action part** tells what the naming part does.	▶ The crowd watches the game. naming part action part

 **Try It!** Read each sentence. Draw a line under the naming part. Circle the action part.

1. The children (play a game).

2. David (plays with marbles).

3. Paula (puts a puzzle together).

4. All the children (help clean the room).

Sentence Parts

GRAMMAR AND USAGE

Practice

Draw a line from each naming part to the correct action part to make a complete sentence.

5. The ball   win the game.

6. Maggie   runs fast.

7. Ben   bounces.

8. The players   throws her ball to James.

Contractions

Rule	Example
▶ Words can be shortened to make contractions. Some letters are taken out. An (') takes the place of missing letters.	▶ was not **wasn't** The (') takes the place of the **o** in **not**.

 **Try It!** Write the contraction on the line.

isn't	I'll	we're	can't

1. I will _____ **I'll** _____

2. cannot _____ **can't** _____

3. we are _____ **we're** _____

UNIT 8   Games • **Lesson 6** *The Great Ball Game*

▶ **Contractions**

Practice

Read each sentence. The underlined words can be shortened. Write the contraction on the line.

it's   She's   hasn't   aren't   don't   we'll

4. We <u>do not</u> like the rain.   **don't**

5. <u>We will</u> play a game.   **we'll**

6. Cory <u>has not</u> played the game.   **hasn't**

7. Now <u>it is</u> Amy's turn.   **it's**

8. <u>She is</u> a good player.   **She's**

9. They <u>are not</u> going outside today.   **aren't**

GRAMMAR AND USAGE

Repeating Sounds

Rule	Example
▶ Writers use words that begin with the same sound.	▶ **S**ea waves **s**plashed and **s**plattered on the **s**eashore. ▶ **C**ats **c**url up on **c**uddly **c**ushions.

Try It! Read the sentence. Circle the words that begin with repeating sounds.

1. (Whirling) (wind) (whisks) the (white) snow into the air.

2. (Seth) (sleds) down the (slippery), (snowy) (slope).

3. (Bob) (bounces) (behind) his (brother).

4. (Greta) (giggles) and (gasps) as she (gallops).

UNIT 8 Games • **Lesson 6** *The Great Ball Game*

▶**Repeating Sounds**

Practice

Draw a picture showing something you like to do. Write a sentence to tell about it. Use words that begin with repeating sounds.

WRITER'S CRAFT

Students should write a complete sentence using at least three words beginning with the same sound.

Cause and Effect

Read each effect. Circle the best cause,
a or **b**.

1. Pam's new coat is all dirty.
   a. It always looks dirty.
   (**b.** She dropped it in a mud puddle.)

2. Tree branches were all over the ground.
   (**a.** A strong wind blew that day.)
   b. Birds were building their nests.

3. Mark's white socks are now pink.
   a. Someone played a trick on him.
   (**b.** They were washed with something red.)

4. Tammy's bike has a flat tire.
   (**a.** She ran over a nail.)
   b. She rode it too much.

5. The puppy was all wet.
   a. It had spilled its water dish.
   (**b.** It had been out in the rain.)

UNIT 8   Games • **Lesson 7** *The Big Team Relay Race*

▶ **Cause and Effect**

COMPREHENSION

Match the sentences that go together.

Effects	**Causes**
6. Margo runs to the field.	The people moved away.
7. Kevin called his grandmother.	It was raining.
8. Sam could not open the lock.	He wanted to wish her a happy birthday.
9. Paula could not find her book.	She is late for soccer practice.
10. That house is empty.	She left it at school.
11. Carol grabbed an umbrella.	Her friend had come to visit her.
12. Sue ran to the door.	Her shoes were too small.
13. Alice's feet hurt.	He had the wrong key.

►Review

►Kinds of Sentences

Read each sentence. Draw a line to the
end mark for each kind of sentence.

1. It is so cold   ?

2. We are building a snowman   !

3. Do you like to play in the snow   .

►Sentence Parts

Draw a line from each naming part
to the correct action part to make a
complete sentence.

4. My hat   melted.

5. Nicole   fell off my head.

6. The snowman   slipped on the ice.

UNIT 8 Games • **Lesson 7** *The Big Team Relay Race*

▶ Contractions   ▶ Review

Draw a line from each pair of words to the correct contraction.

7. she is ———————————— we've

8. we have ———————————— doesn't

9. does not ———————————— she's

Write the correct contraction.

We're	She's	It's	don't

10. _____She's_____ my best friend.

11. I _____don't_____ do anything without my friend.

12. _____We're_____ in the same class.

13. _____It's_____ nice to have a friend.

GRAMMAR AND USAGE

UNIT 8 **Games • Lesson 7** *The Big Team Relay Race*

Organizing a Paragraph That Describes

Rule

▶ Writers use paragraphs to describe objects, people, and places. The first sentence tells what the writer will describe. The other sentences describe it.

Example

▶ Many playgrounds have swings. The frame is made of metal. Two long chains hang from the top steel bar. At the bottom of the chains there is a heavy plastic seat. Swings are a fun thing on a playground.

 **Try It!** Read the paragraph. Circle the sentence that should be first.

Then there is a long ramp from the top to the bottom. It has a metal ladder to climb. Slides are fun if you like to go up and down. (Our playground has a slide.) At the top there are two curved handlebars.

▶ Organizing a Paragraph that Describes

Practice

Look at the picture. Write sentences
to finish the paragraph.

An owl is my
favorite kind of bird.

The paragraphs will vary. Students should write 3–4
sentences describing the picture. The sentences
should reflect the topic sentence that is given.

WRITER'S CRAFT

▶ Review

▶ **Nouns**

Read each sentence. Find and circle nine nouns.

1. (Dillon) and (Kailey) live on a (farm).

2. The (children) feed the (chickens).

3. The (chickens) eat (corn).

4. (Kailey) counts the yellow (chicks).

▶ Pronouns   ▶ Review

GRAMMAR AND USAGE

Read each sentence. Write the sentence using the pronouns at the left.

| They |
| it |

5. Sonya and Robert found a pail.

They found it.

| it |
| She |

6. Sonya put sand in the pail.

She put sand in it.

| He |
| her |

7. Robert helped Sonya build a castle.

He helped her.

| him |
| She |

8. Sonya thanked Robert.

She thanked him.

Drawing Conclusions

Look at each picture. Then answer
each question. Circle your answers.

1. How does Sue feel?
   a. well   (**b.** not well)

2. Why does she feel this way?
   a. She ate too much.
   (**b.** The ride made her dizzy.)
   c. The ride was too slow.

3. How does Christy feel?
   a. sad   (**b.** proud)

4. Why does she feel this way?
   (**a.** She grew the biggest pumpkin.)
   b. The judge is smiling.
   c. She is at the fair.

Read the story. Answer each question with an X. Follow the directions under each question.

Pam rubbed her hands while <u>looking up and down the street</u>. (She pulled her coat) (around her) and (put her hands in her) (pockets.) Sitting on the bench, Pam (shivered) and waited.

5. Where is Pam? inside _____ outside ☒

Draw a line under the words in the story that tell you this.

6. What is it like outside? cold ☒ warm _____

Draw circles around the words in the story that tell you this.

End Rhyme

Rule

▶ A rhyming poem has rhyming words at the end of each line.

Example

▶ A red and green **bug** Creeps across the **rug!**

 **Try It!**

Read the poems. Draw a circle around the rhyming words.

1. A bushy tailed (fox) Jumped out of the (box).

2. Hear bells (ring), Hear birds (sing), While you (swing)!

UNIT 9 Being Afraid • **Lesson 2** *My Brother Is Afraid of Just About Everything*

▶ **End Rhyme**

Practice

Read the poems. Write the rhyming words on the lines.

grab	line	sun	splashes

3. On the sand walks a crab

_____

With its claws ready to __**grab**__ !

4. A big wave crashes

_____

And then it __**splashes**__ !

5. I counted nine

_____

Ducks in a __**line**__ .

6. Three mice run

_____

In the warm __**sun**__ .

▶ Review

▶ Verbs

Read the verbs in the box. Choose the verb that fits each sentence. Write the verb on the line.

climb	rakes	write	jumps

1. Sally __jumps__ rope.

2. I can __write__ my name.

3. Dad __rakes__ the leaves.

4. Mike and Adam __climb__ trees.

▶ **Verbs**

▶ **Review**

Read the sentences. Circle the verb in each sentence.

5. Dad (cooks) the meat.

6. Mom (opens) the basket.

7. Tommy (drinks) his juice.

8. Alice (reads) a book.

9. Aunt Marie (watches) Tommy.

10. I (hide) behind the bush.

GRAMMAR AND USAGE

▶ Review

▶ Kinds of Sentences

Draw a line under the telling sentence.
Circle the asking sentence. Draw a box
around the strong feeling sentence.

1. (Where is the cheese?)

2. [The mouse ate the cheese!]

3. I like cheese.

▶ **End Marks**   ▶ **Review**

Write the correct end mark after each sentence.

4. We are going to Aunt Sue's house.

5. Where does she live?

6. Aunt Sue lives in Ohio.

7. Can we bring our puppy?

8. Aunt Sue just loves puppies!

GRAMMAR, USAGE, AND MECHANICS

Comparing and Contrasting

What is the group of sentences about?
Circle your answers.

1. Suzy is happy, because it is her birthday.

2. Todd is upset, because his toy truck is broken.

3. John is sad because it is raining, and he cannot go outside to play.

(feelings)	the weather

1. People eat apples and bananas.

2. Horses eat oats and grass.

3. Birds eat seeds and worms.

plants	(eating)

► **Comparing and Contrasting**

COMPREHENSION

Circle the word that is different.

1. cat   cat   (coat)   cat

2. worm   (warm)   worm   worm

3. big   big   big   (bag)

4. (boy)   toy   toy   toy

5. read   read   read   (reed)

6. quick   quick   (quack)   quick

7. clue   (cue)   clue   clue

8. blew   (blue)   blew   blew

9. (knot)   not   not   not

10. plain   plain   (plane)   plain

Review

Adjectives

Read each sentence. Draw a line under the words that describe a noun. Circle the noun that they describe. The first one is done for you.

1. It is a <u>cold</u> <u>snowy</u> (day).

2. The <u>big</u> <u>yellow</u> (dog) runs in the snow.

3. Marcy has a <u>fuzzy</u> <u>green</u> (hat).

4. Matthew wears his <u>black</u> (gloves).

5. The children like to play in the <u>fluffy</u> <u>white</u> (snow).

6. They come inside for a <u>hot</u> (drink).

7. Marcy and Matthew sit by the <u>cozy</u> <u>warm</u> (fire).

8. The <u>tired</u> (children) get ready for bed.

UNIT 9 **Being Afraid • Lesson 7** *The Cat and the Mice*

▶ Adjectives That Compare

▶ Review

Read each sentence. Write the correct adjective that compares in the blank.

9. Today is the __coldest__ day of the year.

                 colder   coldest

10. Dan's coat is __warmer__ than mine.

            warm   warmer

11. We made a __bigger__ snowman than Paul.

           biggest   bigger

12. Joan made the __biggest__ snowman in town.

           biggest   bigger

GRAMMAR AND USAGE

Cause and Effect

Read each effect. Circle the best cause,
a or **b**.

1. Mark could not go outside to play.
   a. It was raining heavily.
   b. The front door was broken.

2. The ground outside was white.
   a. Someone poured salt over
   the ground.
   b. It snowed during the night.

3. Pam's cat is licking the milk in the bowl.
   a. The cat is hungry.
   b. The cat is cleaning the bowl.

4. Tom took a long nap.
   a. He was tired.
   b. He was looking for something
   to do.

UNIT 9 Being Afraid • **Lesson 8** *Ira Sleeps Over*

▶**Cause and Effect**

Match the sentences that go together.

Effects	Causes

5. Joe's boots are covered with mud.

It began to drizzle.

6. Dad and Jane took an umbrella.

He had a cold.

7. Jill was late for school.

It was nighttime.

8. Tom blew his nose.

He walked in a mud puddle.

9. Bob scored a home run.

She slept too long.

10. Jen turned on the light.

It was hungry.

11. The dog was barking.

He hit the ball over the fence.

COMPREHENSION

Review

▶ Past Tense Verbs

Read each sentence. Circle the past
tense verb in each sentence.

1. Grandpa and I (drove) to the park.

2. Grandpa (pushed) me on the swings.

3. Then I (ran) to the jungle gym.

4. I (saw) my friend Hannah.

5. She (smiled) at me.

6. We (played) all day.

UNIT 9 Being Afraid • **Lesson 9** *Something Is There*

▶ **Past Tense Verbs**   ▶**Review**

Read each sentence. Write the verb that
tells about something that has already
happened.

7. Amanda and Nick ___**came**___ to the party.

          comes   came

8. The clown **brought** balloons.

     bring   brought

9. The red balloon **popped**.

      popped   pops

10. The children **played** games.

      played   plays

11. Everyone ___**ate**___ snacks.

      eat   ate

GRAMMAR AND USAGE

Rhythm

Rule	Example
▶ Rhythm is the repeated pattern of a beat.	▶ Frogs go leaping. Frogs leap there. Frogs go leaping Just anywhere!

Read the poems. Draw a line to match the poems that have the same rhythm.

1. Rat-a-tat-tat
    Beats the drum.
    Rat-a-tat-tat
    Taps his thumb!

    Bang, bang, bang
    The hammer goes down.
    Bang, bang, bang
    Build houses in town.

2. Tromp, tromp, tromp
    Twenty marching feet.
    Tromp, tromp, tromp
    Up and down the street.

    Drip-a-drip-drip
    Drops the rain.
    Drip-a-drip-drip
    Down the drain.

▶**Rhythm**

WRITER'S CRAFT

Practice

Read the poem. Use the words in the box to write your own poem using the same rhythm.

Mary had a little lamb,
Little lamb, little lamb,
Mary had a little lamb,
Its fleece was white as snow.

dog	play	fluffy	day

_____ _____

Mary had a ____**fluffy**____ ____**dog**____ ,

_____ ____ _____ ____

____**fluffy**____ ____**dog**____ , ____**fluffy**____ ____**dog**____ ,

Mary had a ____**fluffy**____ ____**dog**____ ,

It liked to ____**play**____ all ____**day**____ .

Review

Naming Parts and Action Parts

Read each sentence. Draw a line under the naming part. Circle the verb.

1. <u>Ashley</u> (paints) flowers.

2. <u>Collin</u> (uses) yellow paint.

3. <u>Collin and Ashley</u> (like) art class.

4. <u>They</u> (help) each other.

▶**Agreement**   ▶**Review**

Read each sentence. Write the verb that agrees with the naming part on the line.

5. The baby birds ___sit___ in the nest.

                      sit   sits

6. Spiders ___spin___ their webs.

          spin   spins

7. The bees ___make___ honey in the hive.

     make   makes

8. The frog ___lives___ in the pond.

     live   lives

9. The mice ___hide___ in their hole.

     hide   hides

10. A cow ___rests___ in the barn.

     rest   rests

GRAMMAR AND USAGE

Classifying

Read the words in the box. Then put
them in the correct group.

brick	leaves	wood	nails
twigs	cement	feathers	sticks

Things people use to
build houses:

1. ____**brick**____

2. ____**cement**____

3. ____**wood**____

4. ____**nails**____

Things birds use to
build nests:

5. ____**twigs**____

6. ____**leaves**____

7. ____**feathers**____

8. ____**sticks**____

Read the words in the box. Then pick the two words that go together. Write them on the lines.

paper	night	day	pencil
coat	cat	mittens	kitten

9. _____**paper**_____ and _____**pencil**_____

10. _____**cat**_____ and _____**kitten**_____

11. _____**coat**_____ and _____**mittens**_____

12. _____**night**_____ and _____**day**_____

Classifying

Put an **X** next to each sentence that tells about animals.

1. __X__ Baby frogs are called tadpoles.

2. __X__ The cow grazed on grass in the pasture.

3. ____ Mike threw away the sour milk.

4. __X__ The dog chased the cat around the kitchen.

5. ____ The house is made with bricks.

Classifying

Read the words in the box. Then put them in the correct group.

stove	soup	snow	ice cream
fire	ice cubes	oven	freezer

Things that are hot:

6. _____ **stove** _____

7. _____ **fire** _____

8. _____ **soup** _____

9. _____ **oven** _____

Things that are cold:

10. _____ **ice cubes** _____

11. _____ **snow** _____

12. _____ **ice cream** _____

13. _____ **freezer** _____

COMPREHENSION

UNIT 10 Homes • **Lesson 4** *A House Is a House For Me*

►Review

►Contractions and Apostrophes

Write the contraction on the line. Use an apostrophe to show where letters are missing.

I'm   can't   they've   he's   it's

1. he is

he's

2. they have

they've

3. I am

I'm

4. it is

it's

5. can not

can't

Comprehension and Language Arts Skills

UNIT 10 Homes • **Lesson 4** *A House Is a House For Me*

▶ **Contractions and Apostrophes** ▶ **Review**

Read each contraction. Write the two
words that were put together.

6. wasn't

8. I'll

7. we're

9. didn't

Read each sentence. Circle the two
words that can make a contraction.
Write the contraction on the line.

10. I (have not) seen Meg today.

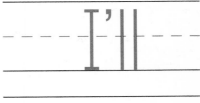

11. (I will) walk to Meg's house.

12. Meg (is not) home.

▶ Exact Words

Rule	Example
▶ Use exact words to add details to your writing.	▶ The **tall oak** tree **towers** above other trees. **Crinkly** bark **wraps** around its **sturdy** trunk. Its **long, slender** branches **sway** in the wind.

Try It!

Read the sentences. Draw a line under the exact words.

1. A <u>yellow</u> <u>daffodil</u> <u>bobs</u> <u>gently</u> in the <u>soft</u> breeze.

2. Five <u>round</u> petals surround its <u>bell shaped</u> flower.

3. <u>Honeybees</u> enjoy <u>sipping</u> its <u>sweet</u> nectar.

4. Its <u>ruffled</u> edges <u>curve</u> to the sides.

Practice

Draw a picture of your house.
Write exact words to describe it.

WRITER'S CRAFT

Students should write sentences that include exact nouns, adjectives, adverbs, or vivid verbs.

Review

▶ Possessive Nouns

Read each sentence. Write the possessive noun in the blank.

1. The bike belongs to Tom.

   It is ___Tom's___ bike.

2. The scooter belongs to Amy.

   It is ___Amy's___ scooter.

3. That toy belongs to the cat.

   It is the ___cat's___ toy.

4. The dog has a bone.

   It is the ___dog's___ bone.

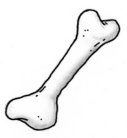

▶ Possessive Pronouns ▶ Review

Read each sentence.
Write the correct
possessive pronoun in
the blank.

Its	Their	Her	His

5. Randy's dad drives the bus.

_____His_____ dad drives the bus.

6. The children's lunches are on the bus.

____Their____ lunches are on the bus.

7. Lori's mom came to help.

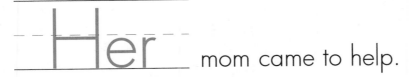

_____Her_____ mom came to help.

8. The elephant's ears are big.

_____Its_____ ears are big.

GRAMMAR AND USAGE

UNIT 10 Homes • **Lesson 6** *Make a Home*

Main Idea and Details

Read the main idea. Then circle the sentence that does not belong.

Main Idea: Weather

Details:

1. The snow was melting in the sunshine.

2. It was so cold that the rain turned into hail.

3. They went swimming in the pool because it was so hot.

4. He had to take a bath because he was covered with dirt.

5. The cool air outside made her nose cold.

6. His mom drove him to school because it was raining.

UNIT 10 Homes • **Lesson 6** *Make a Home*

► **Main Idea and Details**

Read the main idea. Then circle the words that do not belong.

Main Idea: Materials used to make shelters
Details:

wood	dirt	(grapes)
leaves	cement	mud
bricks	nails	cloth
(water)	sticks	ice
reeds	stones	(birds)

COMPREHENSION

Sensory Details

Rule	**Example**
▶ Writers write words that tell how something looks, feels, smells, tastes, and sounds.	▶ Wombats have **white, hairy** noses. They eat **chewy** grass and **soft** roots. Sometimes they make **grunting** sounds.

 **Try It!** Draw a line under the words that tell how something looks, feels, smells, sounds, or tastes.

1. Meerkats make short, sharp, barking sounds.

2. They use their sharp claws to dig.

3. They stay alert in the fresh air.

4. They have round heads and pointed noses.

5. Meerkats eat crunchy beetles.

Practice

Write words to finish the sentences.

| white | rocky | short | loud | cool | black | grassy |

6. Zebras have __**black**__ and

__**white**__ stripes.

7. They make a __**loud**__ whinny sound.

8. Their manes are made of __**short**__ hairs.

9. They drink __**cool**__ water out of the river.

10. Some zebras live in __**rocky**__ hills.

11. Other zebras live on __**grassy**__ plains.

WRITER'S CRAFT

Making Inferences

Look at the picture. Write three
sentences that explain what might
be happening.

1. ___ **The cat wants to eat the fish.** ___

2. ___ **The cat is hungry.** ___

3. ___ **The fish doesn't want to be eaten by the cat.** ___

▶ **Making Inferences**

Read each sentence. Write two possible sentences that explain why each happened.

4. Pat's mother told him to put on his hat and mittens before he went outside.
   Why?

   Answers will vary.
   a. **It was cold outside.**

   b. **It was winter.**

5. Sue went into her bedroom and turned on the light.
   Why?

   Answers will vary.
   a. **She couldn't see in the dark.**

   b. **She was going to read a book.**

COMPREHENSION

UNIT 10 Homes • **Lesson 7** *Home for a Bunny*

▶Review

▶ Quotation Marks

Read each sentence. Underline the exact words someone says. Circle the name of the speaker.

1. "The farm is a busy place," said (Abby).

2. "The hay is in the barn," said (Grandpa).

3. "Where are the horses?" asked (Rita).

4. "The horses are in the stable," replied (Ben).

5. (Abby) laughed, "The pigs are covered in mud!"

Comprehension and Language Arts Skills

UNIT 10 Homes • **Lesson 7** *Home for a Bunny*

▶ Quotation Marks   ▶ **Review**

Read the sentences. Write quotation marks at the beginning and end of the exact words someone says.

6. "May I feed the cows?" asked Rita.

7. "Yes, thank you," answered Grandpa.

8. Abby said, "The hen laid three eggs."

9. "Please gather the eggs in a basket," said Grandpa.

10. Ben rang the bell and yelled, "Dinnertime!"

11. Grandpa sighed, "What a busy day!"

UNIT 10 Homes • **Lesson 8** *Is This a House for a Hermit Crab?*

Structure of a Letter

Rule

▶ A letter has special parts. The parts of a letter are the date, a greeting, a message, a closing, and your name.

Example

▶ (Date:) March 14, 2004

(Greeting:) Dear Shane,

(Message:) We are learning about homes. What are you learning about?

(Closing:) Your friend,

(Your name:) Alex

 **Try It!** Circle the greeting. Draw a line under the date. Draw two lines under the closing. Put a box around the message.

July 6, 2003

(Dear Jamie,)

I went to a play. The actors wore animal costumes. They moved just like real animals!

Your friend,

Teri

▶ **Structure of a Letter**

Practice

Write each part of the letter where it belongs.

Your friend,   Dear Chuck,
Samantha   April 27, 2003

_____

_ _
                              April 27, 2003
_____

_____
_ _
Dear Chuck, _____

We visited the White House. It is where
the president lives. It is a very large house.
Have you ever been there?

_____
_ _
Your friend, _____
_____
_ _
Samantha _____

WRITER'S CRAFT

Reality and Fantasy

Circle Reality or Fantasy.

1. Eddie and Sam put up the tent. (Reality) Fantasy

2. Leo Leopard yelled, "I'm going to jog to the park." Reality (Fantasy)

3. The pig carefully drove the tractor to the cornfield. Reality (Fantasy)

4. Rusty walks his dog Dusty every day. (Reality) Fantasy

5. Wanda Wolf read a bedtime story to her cubs. Reality (Fantasy)

6. Rachel helped Mom fold the clean clothes. (Reality) Fantasy

Reality and Fantasy

Tell if the sentence is real or a fantasy.
Write **R** or **F** in the box.

7. Dennis picked some strawberries.

8. Hannah melts when she walks in the hot sun.

9. A big gorilla sat and stared at us.

10. The two monkeys danced and sang.

11. The ant carried the picnic basket to the park.

12. Two puppies tugged on the old blanket.

13. Missy the mouse went shopping for new shoes.

14. Chris shouted, "Wait for me!"

Review

▶ Capital Letters

Read each sentence. Circle each word
that should begin with a capital letter.

1. (my) friend (marta) is coming to visit.

2. (marta) lives in (new) (mexico).

3. (i) am so excited!

4. (marta) and (i) can ride bikes on
(beech) (street).

5. (she) will be here on (monday).

6. (spending) (july) with (marta) will be fun.

▶ **Capital Letters**   ▶**Review**

Draw a line under the words that should begin with a capital letter. Write the correct capital letter above the word.

7. Uncle <u>greg</u> took us to see fireworks on <u>july</u> fourth.
   G   **J**

8. <u>we</u> saw my friends <u>james</u> and <u>chris</u>.
   W   **J**   **C**

9. <u>i</u> took Marta to <u>jake's</u> <u>pizza</u> for lunch every <u>thursday</u>.
   I   **J**   **P**   **T**

10. It's the best pizza in <u>arizona</u>.
                            A

11. Marta left on a <u>sunday</u>.
                      S

12. <u>i</u> wrote a letter to <u>marta</u> in <u>september</u>.
    I   **M**   **S**

MECHANICS

Audience and Purpose

Rule	**Example**
▶ Writers think about the people they are writing for and what they want to tell them.	▶ A music teacher makes a poster to tell the school about a concert. A store owner makes a sign to tell about a sale.

Draw a line to match the audience to the purpose.

1. people in a restaurant   a recipe

2. a gardener   an ad for a new fishing pole

3. a fisherman   a menu

4. a cook   directions for growing plants

▶ **Audience and Purpose**

Practice

Write the purpose for each audience
on the line.

| write a get well card | invite to a party |
| thank for help | give a report |

5. sick friend _____ **write a get well card** _____

6. many friends _____ **invite to a party** _____

7. a police officer _____ **thank for help** _____

8. your class _____ **give a report** _____

WRITER'S CRAFT